PLANTS OF THE BIBLE

Willard S. Smith
and
Margaret O. Goldsmith

Illustrations by
William Duncan

Abingdon Press

Plants of the Bible

ISBN 0-687-18299-9

Manufactured by the Parthenon Press at
Nashville, Tennessee, United States of America

FOREWORD

The Israelites were an agricultural people, familiar with the fauna and flora of both Palestine and Egypt. It is natural that the Bible should contain hundreds of references to plants.

The ambiguity of certain Hebrew words in the original Scriptures makes accurate identification impossible in some cases. Then too, the early translators, ignorant of certain plants of the Holy Land, applied names of the ones they knew to the Hebrew descriptions.

The Holy Land is a land of contrasts, geographically and weatherwise. The Dead Sea is thirteen hundred feet below sea level; Mt. Horeb is some three thousand feet high. Palm trees flourish in the semitropical climate of the Dead Sea, while only the hardiest of flowers bloom on snow-capped Mt. Hermon. Between these contrasts grow hundreds of plants and trees, and the following pages describe the most common in Hebrew life in Bible times.

Because of its universality, and keeping the above observations in mind, we have used the King James Version for references.

CONTENTS

PLANTS

ACACIA

ACACIA. The acacia is native to Egypt and was known to the early Hebrews, who called it the shittah tree (Isa. 41:19). On the Exodus from Egypt, they carried with them the wood of this tree and used it in building the Ark of the Covenant (Exod. 25:10). Considered sacred, it was never used for other than religious purposes. Some scholars think its spiny growth might have been used to make Jesus' crown of thorns.

ACORUS

ACORUS. Oil pressed from the roots of the acorus was used for anointing. It is a rushlike plant, native to the eastern Mediterranean region. Leaves of the plant were sometimes strewn on the floor of places of worship, in place of carpeting.

ALMOND. Only the olive and the fig are more commonly cultivated in the Holy Land. The pink or white blossoms cover the branches of the almond before the leaves appear as early as January. They resemble peach blossoms, which is not strange since botanically the almond is a member of the peach family. While the nut is universally popular and delicious, it is also crushed to produce almond oil, widely used for flavoring and in cosmetics. Wild almonds grow in some sections of Palestine.

ALMOND

ALOE. Entirely different from the aloes below is the aloe mixed with MYRRH which Nicodemus and Joseph of Arimathea used in preparing the body of Jesus for burial (John 19:38-40). This aloe is a succulent plant with large spikelike leaves, bearing bell-shaped reddish yellow flowers. It is common in the warmer sections of this country. The crushed leaves yield a sap quite commonly used in medicinal lotions.

ALOE

ALOES. The "lign aloes" of Numbers 24:6, also called eaglewood, is a large spreading tree with leaves that resemble those of the peach. The inner wood is soft and fragrant, leading the psalmist to write, "All thy garments smell of myrrh and aloes" (Ps. 45:8).

ALOES

7

ANEMONE

ANISE

APRICOT

ASPALATHUS

ASTRAGAL

BALSAM

ANEMONE. Sometimes called the windflower, the anemone is related to the buttercup. It grows profusely in Palestine. In early spring its vividly colored flowers carpet the plains with color, ranging from white to purple, with the red anemone especially striking. It is believed by many scholars that these were the "lilies of the field" to which Jesus was referring when he told his listeners that "Solomon in all his glory was not arrayed like one of these" (Luke 12:27).

ANISE (dill). When Jesus berated the scribes and Pharisees for confining their holiness to the tithing of "mint and anise" (Matt. 23:23), the reference was most likely to the common dill, since anise was rare in the Holy Land. But the tall feathery plants of dill, with their clusters of small yellow flowers and abundant seed were found everywhere. Even as today, it was used as a spice and for flavoring.

APRICOT. The apricot is one of the most abundant fruits in Palestine. It grows profusely on the highlands and in the lowlands around the Jordan. Since the apple is comparatively recent, the forbidden fruit that grew in the Garden of Eden may well have been the apricot. The Hebrew word translated "apple" in the Song of Solomon 2:3, and the fruit mentioned in Joel 1:12, could have been the golden apricot.

ASPALATHUS. This is a thorny shrub growing from four to five feet high, with narrow leaves along the stem. The very fragrant white and pink blossoms are shaped somewhat like those of the morning glory. From it was derived ointment and perfume. The writer of Ecclesiasticus (24:15) refers to it: "I gave a sweet smell like cinnamon and aspalathus."

ASTRAGAL. This spiny dwarf shrub yields the "gum traga-canth" of commerce. It has pale yellow pea-like flowers and long, needle-sharp thorns which point in all directions. There are many varieties, some found on the shores of the Dead Sea, others high up on the summit of Mount Hermon.

BALSAM. A low-growing tree, the balsam is native to southern Arabia. It is said that the Queen of Sheba brought seeds to King

Solomon, who had groves of balsam planted so that the fragrant and medicinal "balm" made from the sap of the tree might be available. The "balm of Gilead," mentioned several times in the Old Testament (Jer. 8:22; Ezek. 27:17, etc.) is believed by many to be this product of the balsam.

BARLEY

BARLEY. Barley was a common grain when the Israelites were in Egypt. During one of the plagues that beset the land, "the barley was smitten" (Exod. 9:31). It became important in Palestine and is still grown extensively. It is sown in late fall and gathered in the spring. Then a second sowing is made. It was five barley loaves, along with two small fishes, which the lad in John 6:9 gave to Jesus to feed the multitude.

BAY TREE

BAY TREE. David's reference to the "green bay tree" (Ps. 37:35) as a symbol of the spreading power of the wicked is an apt illustration. Actually the spreading comes from the many shoots that sprout near the main stem. It is the "laurel" later used by Rome for the crown awarded the victors in sports and war.

BDELLIUM

BDELLIUM. According to Genesis 2:12, bdellium was planted in the Garden of Eden. It is an ancient tree with small, inconspicuous blossoms and long thorns. From it comes a fragrant gum which, hardening on exposure to the air, forms almost transparent globules with a whitish tinge. Hence the reference in Numbers 11:7, "The manna was as coriander seed, and the colour thereof as the colour of bdellium."

BEAN

BEAN. The bean is an ancient vegetable and has long been a staple article of diet in the Middle East. The bean referred to in II Samuel 17:28 was not unlike the bush bean known to present-day gardeners, though more robust, sometimes growing to a height of two or three feet. The familiar pea-shaped blossoms are white and scented, with a black spot on some of the petals.

The system of voting with white and black balls originated in ancient times when beans were used. Then as now, white showed approval, black signified a No vote.

BETHLEHEM STAR

BETHLEHEM STAR. Though its half-dozen elongated yellow petals that form a "star" appear fragile, the Bethlehem star is a hardy plant. It favors northern exposures and grows in damp, stony ground, blossoming in early winter. This plant is not to be confused with the STAR OF BETHLEHEM.

BRAMBLE

BRAMBLE. The Palestinian bramble (Judges 9:14) is similar to our common blackberry. It is just as strong and has equally numerous sharp thorns. The blossoms have a pinkish tinge. The delicious berries are a deep purple.

BULRUSH

BULRUSH. It was easy to conceal the child Moses among the bulrushes, for they grew thickly along the banks of the Nile, to a height of twelve feet or more. The individual stalks are very pliable, easily made into "an ark" to hold the baby (Exod. 2:3). The blossoms at the top of the long reed resemble a plume of wispy feathers.

CALYCOTOME

CALYCOTOME. The golden color of the calycotome, a gray, prickly shrub, welcomes spring in most regions of the Holy Land. The fragrant yellow blossoms resemble small orchids. The hairy seed pods, much like peapods, begin to ripen as soon as the petals fall, the ripening continuing through the dry summer months. Though used extensively for fencing and fuel, the calycotome is always plentiful, spreading rapidly in dry soil where little other vegetation can survive.

CAMPHIRE

CAMPHIRE. When King Solomon writes, "My beloved is unto me as a cluster of camphire in the vineyards" (Song of Sol. 1:14), we can be sure the camphire is a delightful plant. It is shrublike, about ten feet high, with fragrant creamy-white blossoms that grow in clusters. The camphire is henna, from which comes the rusty-red commercial dye of that name.

CAMPION

CAMPION. Also called Egyptian pink or catchfly, the campion is one of the most common varieties of pinks found in Palestine. Only about six inches high, it grows abundantly around the Sea of Galilee, its blossoming in early February marking the beginning of spring.

CAPER

CAPER. This small inconspicuous plant, bearing white flowers that have rose-magenta filaments with yellow tips, trails over the rocky cliffs so profusely as to cover the ground with its dark green leaves. Thorns grow along the stem. In the familiar passage of Ecclesiastes 12:5 we read, "The grasshopper shall be a burden, and desire shall fail." The original Hebrew reads, "The caper shall fail."

CAROB TREE. While not mentioned by name in the Bible, the carob tree was familiar to the Hebrew people, since it is native to the eastern Mediterranean. An evergreen, it grows up to fifty feet in height. It bears large thick pods used for food—for swine and cattle, and even for people. The "husks" which the swine and the prodigal son ate were very likely these pods, called *locusts*. In the East they are known as "John's bread" and accepted as the "locusts" eaten by John the Baptist (Matt. 3:4).

CAROB TREE

CASSIA. Cassia was one of the "principal spices" which the Lord bade Moses to use in preparing "an oil" with which to anoint the tabernacle (Exod. 30:24f). The spice is made from the bark of the tree. The buds are often used in place of cloves. A purgative is made from the young leaves and seed pods.

CASSIA

CEDAR. One of the best known trees of the Holy Land is the cedar, of which there are several kinds. It is referred to often in the Bible, since it was used for many purposes—from musical instruments to timbers for Solomon's palace.

A smaller cedar is native to the plains of Galilee. It grows only about twenty feet high, with glistening foliage and brown berries instead of cones. This cedar is believed to be the cedar burned in the sacrificial ritual at the temple altar (Num. 19:6).

The cedars of Lebanon are mentioned several times in the Old Testament. Twelve of the oldest and largest are still standing, revered by Christians, Jews, and Mohammedans.

CEDAR

CHRYSANTHEMUM. There is little resemblance between the cultivated chrysanthemum with which we are familiar and the garland chrysanthemum of Palestine. The yellow flower, which blossoms atop the two-foot stem, looks more like a daisy with widespread petals or a small sunflower. It blooms in March.

CHRYSANTHEMUM

CISTUS. The large lavender-pink cistus is a spring flower. It has commercial value, since labdanum, a fragrant gum, is derived from the plant. Some scholars believe that the "myrrh" referred to in Genesis 43:11 was from the cistus.

CISTUS

CLEMATIS. This is also known as buckthorn. Growing in dry, unfertile areas where only a few plants survive, the clematis seems to prepare for a grand exhibit when the rainy season comes. Then the hills are covered with its green-tinted

CLEMATIS

COCKLE

CORIANDER

CORN

CORNFLOWER

COTTON

CRADLEWORT

creamy-white blossoms. Though a shrub, a fully grown plant is almost tree size. The flowers grow at the end of short branches, hanging downward. The bark of the clematis has a sweet taste, of which ants are very fond.

COCKLE. "Let cockle [grow] instead of barley" (31:40) was Job's way of insisting on his integrity, inviting punishment if he were guilty of wrongdoing. Though a rather beautiful plant, some four feet high with veined pink flowers on its spreading stalks, it is a noxious weed. The seeds are poisonous.

CORIANDER. The coriander grows wild in Palestine and was known as early as 1550 B.C. It belongs to the carrot family, but the plants grow to a height of two feet. The leaves resemble parsley. The small white or pinkish blossoms grow in clusters at the end of the flower stems. The seeds are the important part of the plant, since they are pressed for their oil, used for both culinary and medicinal purposes.

CORN. "Corn" in the Bible refers to almost any kind of grain, as it does today in many countries. Our corn was unknown to the people of the Bible.

CORNFLOWER. The Palestinian cornflower is much the same as our familiar bachelor button. It is a deep blue and grows profusely over the hills of much of the Middle East.

COTTON. Cotton is not mentioned by name in the King James Version of the Bible, but later versions describe the hangings in the king's palace as "white cotton curtains" (Esther 1:6). Cotton was grown in Egypt for centuries before the Christian era and was cultivated by the Jews after their settlement in the Holy Land. It was processed much as it was in this country before the advent of the cotton gin.

CRADLEWORT. This is also called Our Lady's bedstraw, legend saying that cradlewort filled the manger in which Mary placed the Christ Child. Some paintings of the old masters show cradlewort in pictures of the nativity. It is a fragile plant, covered with puffs of small, sweet-scented yellow flowers.

CROCUS. This harbinger of spring, blossoming before the snow has gone, was familiar to the people of the Bible. One form is native to the Mediterranean area and no doubt was as eagerly looked for as a sign of spring as it is today.

CROWFOOT. The small glossy yellow blossoms of the crowfoot (often called Jerusalem crowfoot) resemble the familiar buttercup. The finely divided foliage has a grayish tinge. It grows profusely in the rocky soil of Palestine.

CROCUS

CROWN IMPERIAL. Borne at the end of a stiff, upright stem, the drooping flower-cups of the crown imperial are red and yellow. Legend says they were once white, lifted up and blooming in the Garden of Gethsemane. The night Jesus sought the peace of the garden, all the flowers bowed their heads except the proud crown imperial. At the rebuke of Jesus they hung their heads, and red and yellow took the place of the white of innocence.

CROWFOOT

CUMMIN. Cummin has been cultivated since ancient times. It is a small, rather fragile plant about twelve inches in height, with umbels of dainty pink and white flowers. It is cultivated for the seeds, which are crushed and used for flavoring and medicinal purposes. It was valuable enough to be part of the required tithe, but not to be compared with the "weightier matters of the law" (Matt. 23:23).

CROWN IMPERIAL

CYCLAMEN. Growing abundantly throughout much of the Middle East, the cyclamen is called cock of the mountains by the Arabs. It has been dedicated to Mary because the red throat at the heart of the flower looks like a drop of blood, symbolizing the sword of sorrow that pierced Mary's heart when her Son was crucified. It has been described as a strange flower with bent curved petals and crimson eye, looking down as if expecting the earth to yield treasure to it.

CUMMIN

CYPRESS. This is the "gopher wood" referred to in Genesis 6:14, used to build the ark. It was once common on the mountains of Palestine. Because of its great durability it was extensively used for building ships. Gradually the supply was depleted. Since "cypress" and "cedar" are both translations of the same Hebrew word, we cannot always be certain which was intended.

CYCLAMEN

D

DAISY. Although it does not grow as high as our daisy, nor is it as robust, the daisy of the Holy Land bears a close resemblance

CYPRESS

DAISY

DANDELION

DATE PALM

FIG

FIR

otherwise. Its petals are often edged with pink. It is especially abundant in moist areas of the hills, blooming in October and continuing to bloom until the following summer.

DANDELION. Lands bordering the Mediterranean were the original home of the dandelion. From there it spread around the world. In ancient times, as now, the leaves were used in salads. Quite likely it is one of the "bitter herbs" often mentioned in the Bible: the bitter taste of older dandelion leaves is familiar to us.

DATE PALM. It is thought that the date palm may be the oldest known species of tree cultivated by man. After the Exodus from Egypt the Hebrew people took the date palm as a sacred emblem, perhaps because of its importance as a source of food. Also, date palms growing in the desert were an indication of life-giving water in the area. It is the main food supply for man and beast in the desert regions today, as it has been for countless centuries. The palm—there are several varieties—is referred to more than sixty times in the Bible, from Judges 4:5, where we read that "Deborah dwelt under the palm tree" to the waving of palm branches on the first Palm Sunday.

FIG. Ranking with the date palm as one of the most valuable trees of ancient times is the fig. Its pear-shaped fruit was important as food. To the Hebrews this beautiful spreading tree was a symbol of abundance and peace. It is mentioned in Genesis 3:7 as growing in the garden of Eden, and Jesus refers to the fig and the fig tree several times. To the Egyptians it represented the Tree of Life. Its importance to the life and commerce of peoples in the Middle East is still great.

FIR. The fir of the Holy Land is a variety of pine, common in the area west of the Jordan. It is similar to our pines, having silver-gray bark and reddish-brown cones that take on a grayish tinge when fully opened. The needles grow in pairs.

Hiram, king of Tyre, "gave Solomon . . . fir trees" (I Kings 5:10) to be used in the building of the temple. Turpentine and resin were by-products of the fir in ancient times.

FLAG. In Exodus 2:3,5, the flag is mentioned in connection with the hiding of the baby Moses. One of the many plants that thrive in wet ground, it is natural that it be mentioned along with the bulrushes. As Job asks, "Can the flag grow without water?" (8:11).

Entirely different from the swampland flag mentioned above is the corn flag indigenous to Palestine. It grows mostly in the grainfields, its deep pink blossoms changing to purple as they grow older, coloring the fields before the grain ripens in early April.

FLAG

FLAX. The oldest textile fiber in the world is that of flax. From it linen has been made for thousands of years. Probably "linen" is meant in Hosea 2:5, 9, when the prophet mentions "wool and flax." The common flax has a yellowish stem with bright blue flowers. The pink flax is also abundant in the Holy Land, blossoming in late March or early April.

FLAX

FRANKINCENSE. The frankincense tree, source of the spice the magi brought to Bethlehem (Matt. 2:10), resembles our mountain ash. It is a rather large tree with star-shaped pink flowers having yellow centers. The resin, from which comes the incense and spice, is obtained by making incisions in the bark of the tree. As the sap flows out it hardens and becomes brittle. It burns freely, giving off the fragrance for which it is known. Once plentiful in the Near East, it has become increasingly scarce.

FRANKINCENSE

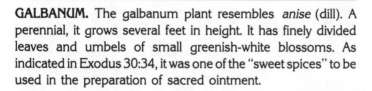

G

GALBANUM. The galbanum plant resembles *anise* (dill). A perennial, it grows several feet in height. It has finely divided leaves and umbels of small greenish-white blossoms. As indicated in Exodus 30:34, it was one of the "sweet spices" to be used in the preparation of sacred ointment.

GALBANUM

GALL. See POPPY.

GERANIUM. We think of the geranium as a cultivated bedding plant in our gardens, growing the year around where winters are warm. In the lands of the Bible it grows wild on the hillsides and in the valleys. It closely resembles our member of the family.

GERANIUM

GLADIOLUS

GLADIOLUS. Called sword lily in Palestine, the native gladiolus derives its name from the curved petals that resemble an eastern scimitar. The blossoms, smaller than our cultivated variety, are pink or purple and grow along one side of the short stem.

GRAPE

GRAPE. Grapes and vineyards are mentioned early and often in the Bible, from Genesis 9:20 to Revelation 14:18, sometimes literally (Deut. 23:24), often as metaphor (Hosea 9:10). While the grapes themselves were of great importance as food and for making wine, the beauty of the vineyards in blossom could not have escaped attention. Except that the harvest began in June, vine culture was much the same in Bible times as now.

HEMLOCK. The hemlock that "springeth . . . in the furrows of the field" (Hosea 10:4) is a poisonous plant, some five feet in height, with dark fern-like leaves. It has small white blossoms in umbels on branching stems. Both seed and plant, when crushed, yield a poisonous substance which can be fatal when taken internally. This was the hemlock Socrates drank.

HEMLOCK

HUMBUM. The Arabs named this plant which decorates the rocky areas of Palestine and neighboring countries. The blossoms, ranging in color from white to blue, cover the tall stalks. The flowers resemble forget-me-nots. The leaves are used as poultices and also as food.

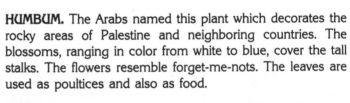

HYACINTH. The blue, bell-shaped flowers of the hyacinth bloom profusely throughout the Holy Land in February and March. They are especially abundant on Mt. Carmel and near Sidon. The smaller grape hyacinth is also found throughout Palestine.

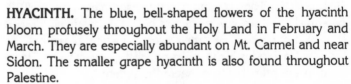

HUMBUM

HYSSOP. Two "hyssops" are referred to in the Bible. David prays, "Purge me with hyssop and I shall be clean" (Ps. 51:7). The reference here, as in other places in the Old Testament, is to an herblike plant belonging to the mint family. It has a pungent taste and a spicy odor. In some Jewish religious rites, it was sprinkled over the sacrifice as a symbolic purifying agent.

HYACINTH

The hyssop mentioned in the New Testament is a member of the sorghum family, sometimes called Jerusalem corn. The large seed heads, ground into meal, constitute the main part of the diet for many people in the Near East. Some scholars believe this was the "parched corn" that Boaz gave Ruth (Ruth 2:14).

The strong stems of the plant grow to a height of six feet or more. This hyssop was used at Calvary when "they filled a sponge with vinegar, and put it upon hyssop, and put it to his mouth (John 19:29).

HYSSOP O.T.

HYSSOP N.T.

J

JUNIPER. The "juniper" mentioned by Job (30:4) and in Psalm 120:4, is an incorrect translation of the Hebrew name for one of the most common flowering shrubs in all Judea. It actually is the flowering broom, a member of the pea family, with pealike clusters of delicate pale pink or white blossoms, followed by pods containing two rows of small, bitter, pealike seeds. It is used extensively as fuel. Although the leaves are small, the plant furnishes a measure of welcome shade in the desert, as when Elijah "came down and sat under a juniper tree" (I Kings 19:4).

JUNIPER

L

LENTIL. The lentil, from which Jacob made the pottage for his weary brother Esau (Gen. 26:29ff.), is a pealike plant resembling vetch. The trailing vine grows in soil too poor for other plants. It is common in most of the Middle East and in Egypt.

LENTIL

LILY. The lily, in many varieties, has been growing in the Holy Land since time immemorial. As far back as 3000 B.C., it was a sacred emblem in Crete. Today it is a symbol of the Resurrection, and of the Virgin Mary. However, our Easter lily is a comparatively recent introduction.

One of the more common varieties in biblical times was the

LILY

LOCUST

LOTUS

LUPINE

MALLOW

MANDRAKE

MARJORAM

brilliant red Chalcedonecum lily, somewhat resembling the modern tulip. Though the lily is mentioned many times in the Song of Solomon and other places in the Bible, we have no way of knowing what variety is meant. Or even if, as in Jesus' reference to "the lilies of the field" (Matt. 6:28), other flowers might have been meant, such as the field ANEMONE.

LOCUST. The locust is the fruit of the CAROB TREE.

LOTUS. When we think of the lotus, we very likely think of Egypt. There it was dedicated to Horus, god of the sun. The Hebrew people must have known of its pagan religious connotation. Perhaps because of that, the lotus never found a place in the symbolism of Judaism or Christianity. It is a water lily, found in many tropical and subtropical countries.

LUPINE. The lupine, which grows profusely in the Holy Land, is almost identical with the familiar variety in our flower gardens. The blue lupine is most common, its striking color covering whole fields in Galilee in the late spring. An unusual characteristic is the hand-shaped leaf.

MALLOW. The mallow, found in swampy places in Palestine, is very much like the thick, downy-leaved plant with which we are familiar. Its purple, pink, and white flowers cover marshy areas. Though not too palatable, the thick fleshy leaves are sometimes used for food by the very poor.

MANDRAKE. A powerful narcotic, the mandrake has been used as an opiate since ancient times. It was also the basis of a "love potion." The creamy white flowers lined with purple give way to small pulpy fruit resembling small tomatoes in shape and color. The large heavy root is forked, and with a little imagination, bears a resemblance to the human body. Probably this is why it is supposed to induce fertility (Gen. 30:1, 14ff.).

MARJORAM. This is one of the smallest flowering shrubs in the Holy Land. Its shrublike stems are only a few inches in height, bearing clusters of white flowers among rocks and wall crevices. It belongs to the mint family.

MINT. Mint of several varieties grows wild in the Holy Land. It is extensively used for flavoring. The Jews believed it efficacious in the treatment of many ailments. It was scattered over the floors of the synagogue, its fragrance scenting the air. Along with RUE and CUMMIN, mint was important enough to be tithed (Luke 11:42).

MINT

MORNING GLORY. The field variety of the morning glory grows over much of the Holy Land. The long trailing vine is quite often seen in fields of grain, its pink and white blossoms coloring the grain stalks.

MORNING GLORY

MOUNTAIN LILY. Though not too abundant, this member of the amaryllis family is found blossoming throughout much of the Middle East. It grows mostly in clay soil. The deep-blue flowers are borne on foot-high stems in clusters of three or four.

MOUNTAIN LILY

MUSTARD. Jesus knew whereof he spoke when he referred to the mustard seed as being "among the least of all seeds" (Matt. 13:32). (Some seeds are smaller.) As he pointed out, it often grows high enough for birds to build nests in it. The yellow-blossom variety is most common, but some kinds have white and lilac blooms. The ground seed furnishes the mustard of commerce.

MUSTARD

MYRRH. The myrrh of the New Testament, included among the three gifts the magi brought to the Christ Child, was an aromatic made from the resin of the thorny, bushlike tree. The thick white gum, which exudes when the bark is pierced, hardens on exposure to the air and becomes reddish in color. It has been used as a spice or as medicine since ancient times. The Hebrews used it as one of the ingredients of the anointing oil for the tabernacle, and in the preparation of the dead for burial. Hence Nicodemus brought "a mixture of myrrh and aloes" to be sprinkled over the linen clothes with which he wound the body of Jesus (John 19:39).

MYRRH

MYRRH (O. T.). See CISTUS.

MYRTLE. To the Egyptians, Greeks, and Romans, the evergreen myrtle was sacred and used in their worship. While not sacred to the Hebrews, it was revered. The tent of the tabernacle was covered with blooming boughs of myrtle.

MYRRH

MYRTLE

Isaiah mentions it as one of the trees that God "will plant in the wilderness" (Isa. 41:19). And the familiar 55th chapter of Isaiah closes with the promise that "instead of the brier shall come up the myrtle tree." Sometimes it is a bush, but again it may grow to be a twenty-foot tree. The white blossoms are fragrant, and the aromatic fruits are dried for perfumes and spices.

NARCISSUS

NARCISSUS. Our common pollyanna narcissus is one of the common spring flowers in Bible lands, growing profusely on the plains of Sharon and Jericho. It is quite generally agreed among scholars that this common but fragrant and beautiful flower may be the ROSE of Sharon in Song of Solomon 2:1.

NETTLE

NETTLE. The nettle of the Holy Land grows as high as five feet, with nearly two feet of blooms on the flower stem. This height is indicated by Job when he berates those who have failed him: "Under the nettles they were gathered together" (30:7). It is a perennial, its spine-tipped leaves protecting it from mauraders. Still, the lavender-streaked white flowers are beautiful—even if not gathered!

OAK

OAK. The veneration of the oak by the ancients was not lost on the Hebrews. Mention of the fact that Deborah was buried beneath an oak (Gen. 35:8) and that Gideon received "an angel of the Lord" under the branches of an oak (Judges 6:11) indicate that it had a special significance. Several varieties of the tree grow in Palestine, varying with the altitude and the soil. The expression "as strong as an oak" was as apt a simile when Amos recorded those words (2:9) as it is today.

OLEANDER

OLEANDER. The tall oleander—it may grow as high as twenty feet—is one of the most beautiful shrubs in Palestine when in full bloom. The flowers cover a wide range of colors, from white, rose, red, to purple. They blossom in the spring and last all summer. It is an evergreen, easily grown. Unfortunately, flowers and plant alike are highly poisonous; even the smoke from the burning leaves is wisely avoided.

OLIVE

OLIVE. Asia Minor is believed to be the original home of the olive, which has been cultivated for thousands of years. It was an olive "branch" (twig) that the dove brought back to Noah on the ark. Jesus left the upper room and "went out unto the Mount of Olives" (Matt. 26:30).

Olive trees always have been of practical value—the fruit for food, the oil pressed from the fruit for ancient lamps. And when Samuel poured oil over the head of David to anoint him, he was following a ritualistic custom.

ONION

ONION. The onion and its culinary cousin, the leek, was widely used for food even before biblical times. In the warm, dry weather of Palestine the cultivated onion grows very large and is very sweet. There are many wild varieties. Some, like the pink onion—the color of the blossom giving it its name—grow in rocky places to a height of three or four feet.

ONYCHA. Mentioned with the sweet spices "stacte" (STYRAX) and "GALBANUM" in Exodus 30:34, we know that the onycha was a source of aromatic resin from which is produced labdanum. It is a three foot bush with large flowers having five white petals, each with a spot of scarlet that darkens near the center with stamens and pistil. Also known as the rock rose, it blossoms profusely during the long dry season.

ONYCHA

ORCHID. Orchids may seem out of place in the Holy Land, and the familiar tropical species is not found there, but a dozen or more species are common. The monkey orchid and the earth-wasp orchid are abundant in rocky soil. One of the most common varieties is the Antoilan orchid, with several rather small pink blossoms on a stem, of typical orchid shape. It blooms in March.

ORCHID

P

PANNAG. This is a variety of millet which, though not as palatable as wheat or barley, was used extensively for food

PANNAG

POMEGRANATE

POPPY

REED

RESURRECTION
PLANT

RIE

among the common people, especially in time of famine (Ezek. 4:9). One stalk may produce thousands of seeds. They are hard and white and are ground into flour (Ezek. 27:17).

POMEGRANATE. Growing wild in some sections of the Middle East, the pomegranate is a small tree with reddish bark, shiny green leaves, and waxlike blossoms with crinkled, coral-red petals. The ripe fruit is about the size of an orange, maroon, with thick skin and many seeds. The juicy pulp is very palatable.

The popularity of the pomegranate is indicated by the fact that they were used as figures in the decoration of Solomon's temple (I Kings 7:18,20). Pomegranate designs were braided into the hem of the ephod of the high priest (Exod. 28:33,34).

POPPY. The poppy of the Orient, the source of opium, was common in the Holy Land long before the Israelites settled there. The "gall" added to the vinegar and offered to Jesus (Matt. 27:34) was the juice of the opium poppy. This gesture may have been intended as an act of mercy, since gall is a powerful narcotic. The rather fragile lavender or white blossom with a spot of purple at its base belies the sinister nature of the seed pod from which the opium is extracted.

REED. One of the marsh plants common to the Middle East, the "reed" referred to in Ezekial 40:3 very likely was the variety phragmites. The stems of this reed were used for measuring. As with most similar plants, it grows to a considerable height, twelve feet or even more being common. The silky purple plume is often used for decoration.

RESURRECTION PLANT. This plant, often available at our florists, is sometimes called the rose of Jericho. When withered, it closes into a ball, apparently lifeless, and blows over the sands "like a rolling thing before the whirlwind" (Isa. 17:13). Finding moisture, it sends out roots, unrolls, and grows again.

RIE. In the plague of hail that fell upon Egypt, "the wheat and the rie were not smitten for they were not grown up" (Exod. 9:32). A natural conclusion might be that rye was meant. But *rie* is correct. It is a grain closely resembling wheat, though much taller and able to grow and produce in very poor soil. Though the rie flour was inferior to that of wheat, it was extensively used, the two often being mixed, along with barley (Isa. 28:25).

ROSE

ROSE. Wild roses are not too common in Palestine. The thicket rose, a dainty pink and white variety, climbs over the rocks of the hill country, blooming in the spring. A tall climbing variety with white blossoms grows in Galilee. The Phoenician rose, a tall bush with clusters of single white flowers, grows in the higher regions of the Holy Land.

The "rose of Sharon" (Song of Sol. 2:1) is probably a poetic expression. Or it might have been the TULIP or NARCISSUS.

RUE

RUE. One of the herbs Jesus mentions in his denunciation of obeying only the letter of the law (Luke 11:42) was rue. It is a tall plant bearing clusters of yellow flowers with a knob of green. It was widely used as a disinfectant—its botanical Latin name means "strong smelling"—and also for medicinal purposes. Its strong, unusual taste apparently appealed to the ancients who used it as a flavoring.

RUSH

RUSH. Many varieties of rush grow along the river banks and in the swampy areas of the Holy Land. Any one of these might be indicated in Bildard's query, "Can the rush grow without mire?" (Job 8:11). A common variety is the bob rush, a grasslike plant growing over four feet high. The leaves are long and slender, cylindrical in shape, widely used to make mats and baskets.

S

SAFFRON

SAFFRON. The lavender-colored saffron resembles the crocus, though larger, and blooms in the fall. In biblical times, as today, the orange stigmas are the source of the saffron of commerce, used as a condiment, as perfume, a coloring ingredient, and in medicines.

SALVIA

SALVIA. The Jerusalem salvia, though of the same botanical family as our familiar red salvia, is quite different in appearance. It has the characteristic square stem, but the blossom stems are spaced so that the individual flowers stand out, resembling tiny

23

SILVERWEED

SMILAX

SPANISH BROOM

SPEEDWELL

SPIKENARD

STAR OF
BETHLEHEM

orchids, rather than the spike of solid bloom we know. It is thought by some to be the source of the design for the seven-branched candlestick common to the Jews.

SILVERWEED. This humble plant grows along the dusty wayside, its silvery fernlike leaves pressed flat against the ground, its small yellow flowers giving a bit of color to its drab surroundings.

SMILAX. The prickly smilax of the Holy Land is a close relative of the smilax we know. The very small greenish-white blossoms appear in October and November, followed by brilliant scarlet berries. These remain on the branches and are used for decoration much as we use sprigs of holly.

SPANISH BROOM. Sometimes called prickly asparagus, the Spanish broom grows in the woods in all countries of the Mediterranean area. It is a shrub, peculiar with its long, grooved stems, widely used for weaving nets and baskets. The bright yellow flowers along the stems somewhat resemble small orchids.

SPEEDWELL. The white and blue speedwell is common throughout the Middle East. It is an early bloomer, three or four inches high, blanketing much of the otherwise barren landscape in early February.

SPIKENARD. The spikenard which the woman poured over the head of Jesus (Mark 14:3) was indeed "very precious." One pound cost three hundred dinarii, nearly a year's wages. The spikenard plant is odd in appearance. The lower stems have a hairy covering from which grow the flower stems and leaves. The blossoms are red with a sweet fragrance. But the perfume, for which the plant is best known, comes from the hairy stem. To preserve its fragrance, spikenard is still transported in alabaster boxes, mentioned by Mark.

STAR OF BETHLEHEM. This plant is different from the BETHLEHEM STAR, though both do belong to the lily family. It is a spring-blooming plant with white six-petaled flowers on the end of six-inch stems. The bulb is sometimes roasted for food or ground into flour. It is strange that such a lovely flower should be called by the rather inelegant name used in II Kings 6:25—"dove dung."

STYRAX (or storax). The white clusters of drooping flowers of the styrax are very fragrant and appear in March or April. The styrax is a shrub that may grow as high as twenty feet on the hills around the Jordan and is especially abundant in Galilee. It is revered by the Palestinians, so much so that it is almost a calamity if one is cut down. Legend says that Moses, on leaving Egypt, made his staff of the styrax. Resin from the plant is used in medicine.

STYRAX

SYCAMINE. This is the black mulberry tree, the fruit closely resembling large blackberries. Familiar to the Hebrews while in Egypt, it is known also in the Holy Land. Jesus referred to the sycamine tree that "faith as a grain of mustard seed" could move (Luke 17:6).

SYCAMINE

SYCAMORE. About the only resemblance to this tree and the sycamine mentioned above is the spelling and the pronunciation. Both are mentioned in the New Testament, which accounts for the confusion. The sycamore is a variety of fig of very poor quality. The figs grow close to the boughs and trunk of the tree. The large trunk separates into several branches quite close to the ground, making it easy for Zacchaeus to climb the sycamore tree that he might better see Jesus (Luke 19:4).

SYCAMORE

TAMARISK. Possibly influenced by the fact that it was sacred to the Arabs, Abraham planted a tamarisk tree at Beersheba (Gen. 21:33). It is a small evergreen with white flowers, flourishing in areas of very low rainfall. Thousands of tamarisk trees have been planted in the desert-dry regions, following the example set by Abraham.

TAMARISK

TARE. Jesus' parable of the tares in the wheat field (Matt. 13:24-30) was so true to life that his listeners could not fail to understand his meaning. The plant referred to is bearded darnel, or rye grass. It so closely resembles the wheat plant during growth that it is difficult to tell the two apart until the grain heads appear, hence the point of Jesus' parable. Winnowing the grain blows away most of the lighter seeds of the tares. Any remaining are disposed of when the grain is shaken in a sieve, the smaller tare seeds falling through the mesh.

TARE

THISTLE. "Do men gather grapes from thorns or figs from

THISTLE

THORNS

THYNE TREE

TULIP

VETCH

thistles?" (Matt. 7:16). Jesus' listeners, quite familiar with the pestiferous thistle, must have smiled at the aptness of his question. Thistles are mentioned as early as Genesis 3:18, and often in the Old Testament (I Kings 14:9; II Chron. 25:18; Hos. 10:8; Job 31:40, etc.). The downylike blossoms are lovely, but the stinging leaf hairs are its universal trademark.

THORNS. It is said that in no other country are there as many thorny plants as in the Holy Land. There are some forty references to thorns in the Bible, and many more if we include the often-used "brier." It is natural that most interest centers around the one that composed Jesus' "crown of thorns." Many scholars believe it was the paliurus, a common shrub growing from three to nine feet high, bearing tiny white blossoms and long, recurved thorns.

THYNE TREE. John, writing from Patmos, mentions "thyne wood" among the merchandise that "the merchants of the earth shall . . . weep over" (Rev. 18:11,12). Also known as citronwood, it is a conifer, resembling our arborvitae. The fragrant wood was burned as incense and also highly prized for woodwork, as it is almost indestructible.

TULIP. It is not strange to find the tulip growing wild in the Holy Land, since it is native to nearby Persia. The tulip common in Palestine blooms early in the spring, as tulips do the world over. It is generally a striking red with pointed petals. It is believed that the tulip, growing profusely on the plain of Sharon, may be the "rose of Sharon" mentioned in the Song of Solomon 2:1. The literal translation of the original Hebrew word lends credence to this belief, since it indicates that a bulb-growing plant was meant, not a shrub.

VETCH (or vetchling; fetch). The vetch, or vetchling, of the Holy Land resembles our common variety. There, as here, its slender climbing stem grows in the fields of grain, attaching itself to the stalks. There are several varieties of vetch in Palestine. The charming vetchling is especially attractive, with small orange-pink blossoms that look like sweet peas. Other varieties are blue.

$\mathcal{W}$

WHEAT

WHEAT. Wheat is the most universal of all grains, so old that there is no record of when or where it originated. Keeping to the custom common today in most European countries, the English translators used "corn" where grain, including wheat, was referred to, as in Genesis 41:1,5-7, when Pharaoh dreamed of seven full ears, then seven thin ears of "corn." Corn was unknown, but there was a variety of wheat with seven "ears," or heads of grain.

WORMWOOD

WORMWOOD. Wormwood is sometimes linked with gall (see POPPY) as in Deuteronomy 29:18 and Jeremiah 23:15, an indication of its natural bitterness, especially of the leaves, which are used medicinally. It is a small shrub with small buttonlike yellow flowers.

GROWING
A BIBLICAL GARDEN

We are not as dependent on what we ourselves grow for food, shelter, and raiment as were the pastoral people of the Bible. But by tending a few plants like theirs, we may link ourselves in spirit with the time when trees, herbs, flowers, and shrubs were symbols of the eternal truths of the Bible and stood for peace, security, joy, beauty, and holiness—or the opposites—to those who lived in those days.

POTTING BULBS IN THE FALL

TULIP

Did you know that the hardy forerunners of modern tulips, narcissus, hyacinths, and crocus grew wild on the bleak hillsides of Palestine for centuries before the Christian era? Suddenly after spring rains, they carpeted the terrain with a burst of bloom. The Hebrew word for *rose* has as its root a word which means *bulb*. So when Isaiah said, "The desert shall . . . blossom as the rose," he was not referring to any rose as we know it, but to the wild red tulip and early narcissus, the first bulbs to appear in the spring. The wild rose of Damascus bloomed later, with small flowers.

NARCISSUS

Be sure to include our early Red Emperor tulip among the bulbs you force, and a few yellow *Jonquilla narcissi simplex* or the bunch-flowered *Narcissus tazetta,* listed also as *poetaz.* Both have clusters of little flowers, several to a stem. You will want also a pot of hyacinths, as both the single- and double-flowering blue and white kinds were common to the Holy Land long before travelers took them to Europe.

Soak your choice of hardy bulbs in disinfectant and allow a cushion of sand under each, as you pot them in a mixture of ½ good topsoil, ¼ humus, and ¼ sharp sand, with a teaspoon of bone meal to each pot. Allow six crocus, four or five tulips and three or four narcissus or hyacinth bulbs to each shallow pot. Water the pots and label them. Then pack the pots two inches apart in a box of peat moss, kept damp, and set the box, covered with burlap, in an unheated area in the house.

After six weeks, uncover the box and take out any Roman

CROCUS

HYACINTH

hyacinths you potted. Wait three weeks more, then see if roots have come through the holes at the bottom of the other pots. If so, bring in one pot and let the others stay two weeks longer, to prolong the display. At first, keep the bulbs you bring indoors at 45° temperature. Water as needed, and after ten days, expose them gradually to more sun and heat each day. Fit paper cones over hyacinths and tulips to stimulate stem growth, until flower spikes are three to four inches high. Then remove the cones.

To grow hyacinths in a vase of water, set the vase in a cool, dark, airy place, with the bulb base just above the water level. When the roots fill the container, put it in a warmer, sunny room.

When hardy bulbs finish blooming and the leaves turn brown, let the pots dry out. Then store the bulbs in dry sand until you plant them outdoors in the spring.

LILY

Lilium candidum, which legends call the Madonna or Easter lily, is easy to force indoors. Botanists have found that this white lily, now almost extinct in Judea, may have grown wild there when Christ was born. The Italian painters of the Middle Ages, who developed the legend by showing the lily in their scenes of the Annunciation, assumed that the sacred lily was common to early Palestine, as it was to medieval Europe.

In forcing this stem-rooting bulb, fill a six-inch pot only half full of the soil for other hardy bulbs and add a teaspoon of plant food, sifted in through a sieve. Set in one lily bulb just below the surface. Water it and keep it with other hardy bulbs in a cold place for twelve weeks. Then bring it into a cool room, water it, and add an inch of the soil mixture to the pot each week, for the roots to grow in. The care of an Easter lily is otherwise the same as for other bulbs, but screen it from drafts and spray it for aphids with oil spray. It can dry in the shade outdoors in the summer. Repot it to force again next September.

BULBS AND TUBERS
TO START INDOORS

SAFFRON

Meadow saffron, an autumn-blooming crocus listed as *Colchicum autumnale* and called "saffron" in Song of Solomon 4:14, was and still is prized for its perfume and its commercial use as the golden dry saffron, made from the stigmas of its blossoms. In late August, pot up a few bulbs in a low bowl, barely covered with the soil for hardy bulbs. Do not chill them. Keep them in a moist, warm, shady room until the stems and roots develop. Then give them sun. Its flowers of yellow or lavender bloom in a few weeks without leaves. After flowering, plant the bulbs in late October, one inch deep, in a sunny border.

In October you can start, as for saffron, the low-growing bulbous *Iris reticulata,* another flower of Bible times, in a shallow planter. After ten weeks at 65° temperature, by Christmas it will bloom with the fragrance of violets. The hardy variety of dwarf Star of Bethlehem, listed as *Ornithogalum umbellatum,* still makes a sheet of starry white flowers on the hills of Palestine. These bulbs, used for food, were called "dove's dung" in II Kings 6:24-25. Pot a few in a window planter with the soil for Easter lilies. Given a 65° temperature for around ten weeks, they will bloom with *Iris reticulata.* Plant both kinds of bulbs in the rock garden in April, in light alkaline soil to naturalize and bloom there next spring.

STAR OF BETHLEHEM

The exotic, large flowers of anemone and ranunculus make the most showy outdoor display of all tuberous plants, in mild climates like the Holy Land and California. We can be almost certain that they are what Jesus referred to as "the lilies of the field." It was because of the anemone's purple, rose, red, and blue petals and black centers that he said, "Solomon in all his glory was not arrayed like one of these." In early September, we can plant tubers of the Bride and St. Brigid varieties to force for about eight weeks before flowering. Ranunculus tubers can be started later at intervals, for their globes of orange, red, and gold blooms from February to May.

ANEMONE

Soak the tubers of anemones and ranunculus for twenty-four hours in warm water. Then plant them four to six inches apart, 1½ inches deep, in ten-inch containers, in a soil mixture of ¼ good topsoil, ¼ leaf mold, ¼ peat moss, ¼ sharp sand. Stir through each potful of soil one tablespoon of plant food. Set the containers in a cool room, not over 45° temperature, where they get morning sun. Keep the soil moist until growth is established, then water less often until buds form. From then through flowering, anemones and ranunculus need plenty of water and sun and more heat, but never over 65° temperature.

After blooming, the plants need less water and the foliage will gradually die down. Then lift the tubers, rest them in a cool place, packed in a bag of dry sand, for two months or more. They can be planted again in fresh soil next season.

HERBS FOR THE WINDOW GARDEN

Gardens of herbs are mentioned several times in the Bible, as in I Kings 21:2. Every landowner had such a garden and included cucumber, watermelon, and muskmelon vines. The herbs were essential: the flax for making linen cloth; some for

ANISE

CORIANDER

FLAX

MUSTARD

flavoring food; others for spices, medicines, and perfumes. Some annual Bible herbs are anise, coriander, sium, dill, flax, mustard, and fennel. Botanists doing research on Bible plants list two other annual herbs native there—common basil and the castor bean.

You can raise dill and basil from seed as culinary herbs for use in salads. The basil leaves are also good in cool drinks and, when dried, in herb tea. The flax *(Linum usitatissimum),* with its blue flowers, has decorative value in an outdoor raised bed. It is the commercial source of linen cloth and flaxseed oil now, as in biblical times. The castor bean has large ornamental, deeply cut leaves and showy seed pods. It is useful as a house plant and germinates from seed in two weeks. Authorities now think that besides being the source of a laxative oil in ancient Judea, where the castor bean grows very tall, it also was the tree that grew up during the night, called a "gourd" in the story of Jonah (4:6).

ANNUAL HERBS: Sow herb seeds in August, with the rows two inches apart, in self-watering seed pans of ⅔ topsoil and ⅓ sharp sand firmed down with a board, under a ½-inch top layer of screened, shredded sphagnum moss, which prevents dampening off of seedlings. Cover the pan with glass and newspaper, and keep it at 70° temperature for two or three weeks until the seeds germinate.

Then remove the paper. Wipe the moisture off the glass and put it back with a narrow opening for ventilation. Increase the exposure to light gradually, and decrease the heat a little. When the seedlings reach the glass cover, remove it. Feed them weekly with a plant food solution (2 teaspoons to a gallon of water) until they are ready to pot in the soil mixture for bulbs over a base of pebbles. Add to the mixture ½ teaspoon per pot of plant food and ½ teaspoon of ground lime. Use china, metal, or plastic containers for herbs, as clay pots dry out too fast. Set the plants in a sheltered corner of a cool room and condition them gradually to sunlight, a lower night temperature, and less water.

PERENNIAL HERBS: For winter use indoors, before cold weather pot up the plants of herbs you can buy in September or have raised from seed started at Easter time. Start these the same as annual herbs. Use the same potting mixture, except for bay leaf.

The Scriptures mention specifically the following seven: (1) bay leaf *(Laurus nobilis)* called "green bay tree" in Psalm 37:35; (2) the leeks, onions, and garlic of Numbers 11:5, 6, all *alliums,* which we can represent by chives; (3) pot marjoram *(Origanum vulgare)*, the best herb for us to substitute for the hyssop in Psalm 51:7, since botanists know it grew in Palestine and corresponds to the Bible use for hyssop (what we call hyssop today originated in Europe); (4) mint, evidently the common peppermint; (5) common rue; (6) spikenard, not available here except as garden heliotrope *(Valeriana officinalis)*, a member of the same herb family; (7) wormwood *(Artemisia absinthium),* the variety indicated in Jeremiah 23:15. Four other available perennial herbs grown in Israel during Bible times are lavender, horehound, rosemary, and common thyme.

MINT

Below are the outstanding features of the less familiar of these perennials (those with asterisks are *not* hardy outdoors in northern winters).

Bay leaf*—has sweet-smelling evergreen leaves, is used as a condiment and in medicines. It needs the soil mixture for bulbs, but stir into each six-inch potful 1½ teaspoons of plant food that has been sieved. It develops into a desirable tub plant if kept during winter on a sunny enclosed porch. Water it often. In the spring, set it on the terrace, mulch with plant food, and prune as needed.

MARJORAM

Pot marjoram *(Origanum vulgare)*—has purple flowers and aromatic leaves, is used to season meat. It grows to be sixteen inches high.

Rue—was called the herb of grace by early Christians and associated with repentance. It has yellow flowers in summer and strong-scented blue-green fernlike leaves, used not only in perfumes for centuries but for its almost magic power in medicines.

RUE

Valerian—The common variety known as garden heliotrope can be planted in our perennial border to add fragrance and blend with more showy flowers. The species known as the spikenard of Bible times had a stronger odor in both stems and roots and was used to make perfumed ointments, such as Mary brought to anoint the feet of Jesus in John 12:3-9.

Wormwood *(Artemisia absinthium)*—has a bitter flavor to its silky, grey-green, finely divided leaves. It was used as a tonic in Judea and was the symbol of bitter suffering to the soul (see Rev. 8:11).

WORMWOOD

Lavender*—The English variety has tall spikes of sweet-smelling flowers that yield the seeds still used to scent linen and bath water, and in perfumes as when Paul preached to the Romans.

Thyme—The true culinary variety, called *Thymus vulgaris,* is an erect plant only six to eight inches high. Its odor is the symbol of ageless sweetness.

Rosemary*—of the common variety is a tall plant, often called the herb of remembrance because of the unforgettable fragrance of its leaves and flowers. The leaves are used to flavor soups; their oil is used in perfume.

Horehound—has square stems and woolly white leaves; whorls of flowers have sharp bracts on their lobes. The juice made from boiling the plants was and still is used as a remedy for colds.

All herbs need sun and moist soil and fresh air. They resent gas fumes or stale water standing on their roots, so use containers with drainage holes and empty the saucers under them often. Three inches of pebbles may be placed below the soil, if the herbs are in dishes without holes. Open the windows near herbs on mild days. A kitchen-window shelf is a good place for culinary herbs, unless the cooking fuel is gas.

THE HOME TREES AND VINES OF BIBLE TIMES

A home was not a home to the ancient Hebrews without its fig tree, its olive, its grape vine, a date palm for fruit and shade, its pomegranate, and so-called apple tree. These all stood for God's bounty and mercy and inner peace, such as the olive branch brought by the dove gave Noah. They signified security from hunger and outer stress and shelter from the blazing sun. If "the vine is dried up, and the fig tree languisheth," then doom descends and, as Joel put it, "Joy is withered away from the sons of men" (1:12).

FIG

You can buy seeds or plants of fig and pigmy date palms. Sow the fig seeds in February in a shallow, oblong dish, with a layer of pebbles and charcoal below the same soil mixture used for herbs, and a top layer of sphagnum moss. Moisten the soil and put glass and paper over the top. Keep at an even 70° temperature until the seeds germinate. Then remove the glass and tend as for herbs. The glossy-leaved fig seedlings, kept watered, make an attractive table display where they get sun. When three inches high, they can be thinned out and the best ones potted separately, over drainage pebbles and broken clay pots, in the same soil mixture used for bulbs, enriched and mulched with plant food as for bay leaf. Sow date-palm seeds like the fig, but in a larger container, such as a window box.

OLIVE

The feathery Phoenix date palms, or Neanthe bella, and dwarf fishtail palms can be kept compact. They resist our hot-dry rooms in winter and thrive best in semishade, in six- to seven-inch well-drained pots that crowd the roots. Overwatering is fatal. Their leaves need to be wiped free of dust and scale weekly with a moist, soapy sponge. In summer, set them out, protected from wind and shaded by trees.

GRAPE

In the winter, as the figs develop with their interesting five-lobed leaves, they need a cooler place than palms, and plenty of water outdoors during spring and summer. They produce fruit even when young and growing in an eight-inch bucket.

There are two small-leaved, clinging varieties of fig *(Ficus pumila* or *Ficus radicans)* for year-round indoor use, whether planted with a slab of wood to climb on or allowed to train over the edge of the container. Never let the soil dry out. Provide moisture in the air, from trays of water over radiators or steam from teakettles.

DATE PALM

The hardy Russian olive is the Bible variety we can grow indoors. The Garden of Gethsemane, where Jesus spent his last night, was a grove of olive trees. Olive oil was the source of light in altar lamps, eaten like butter on bread, and used in anointing honored guests. Hosea (14:6) speaks of the beauty of the olive. It has fragrant flowers and needs sun and a cool room in winter, average soil, and when it becomes full-grown, can be planted outdoors as a good lawn tree.

The grape vine, so important in Israel, can be grown as a vine over an arbor outdoors, but indoors we can represent it by a tough little trailing or climbing plant of the grape family called the Cape grape *(Cissus capensis).* It likes an east window in a hanging pot with the same soil used for bulbs, kept moist, and may need its three-lobed, rust-colored leaves wiped free of mealy bugs occasionally.

POMEGRANATE

The pomegranate *(Punica granatum)* was the emblem of fertility to Israelites because of the many seeds inside its showy red fruit. A spiced wine was made from its juice. Solomon's Song, 4:13 and 6:11, mentions an orchard of pomegranates. Their bell-shaped flowers were part of the design embroidered on Aaron's coat.

In the spring you can buy a small pomegranate of a twiggy, bushy variety. Its fluffy red double blossoms should appear the second year. Give it the same soil as bulbs, over drainage pebbles. Keep it well watered from February through flowering. Trimmed into a tree shape, it makes an ornamental house plant and a hardy fruit tree outdoors as far north as Washington, D.C.,

APRICOT AND CITRUS FRUITS
AS TUB PLANTS

APRICOT

The apple tree of Bible times was not the fruit tree we know by that name, which has been developed since 1800. Practically any fruit was called "apple" by the translators of the Scriptures. Since the fruit is often said to be golden, as in Proverbs 25:11, authorities now consider that the apricot *(Prunus armeniaca)* was meant, since it grew before the Christian era in Syria. Or it might mean the orange or any other citrus fruit of ancient Palestine. Choose any of these for your tub garden.

Apricots as house plants have pink blossoms in the spring and an attractive form, but no fruit. Get a dwarf, two-year-old one early in April. Plant it over pebbles in the soil for bulbs, in a pot with drainage holes, as apricots cannot survive stale water standing on their roots. Water sparingly in the winter and keep the plant on an enclosed porch. In hot weather, set it out in the sun,

OTAHEITE
ORANGE

mulched with peat moss. Otaheite orange trees, dwarf lemons, and Calamondin citrus trees make desirable house plants. You will enjoy their fragrant blossoms, shiny leaves, and decorative fruit. They take the same soil and care as apricots. Spray them with oil spray for scale. Sink the pots in the ground in summer.

BULRUSHES AND A WATER
GARDEN IN A TUB

LOTUS

BULRUSH

The story of Moses hidden in the bulrushes serves as the theme for a tub garden in which to plant water lilies, the large pink Egyptian lotus, a cattail or flowering rush, and sweet flag. Next to it, set a pot of papyrus, which the Bible calls bulrush. This towering plant, *Cyperus papyrus,* from which the scrolls of paper found in ancient tombs were made, is a picturesque house plant. It can be planted in a redwood container on rollers, with an overflow section to catch water so it can be taken indoors in the winter.

There is a dwarf papyrus suited to small rooms. Aromatic

sweet flag *(Acorus calamus)* is considered by botanists to be the source of the holy ointment of the tabernacle, referred to in Exodus 30:23 as calamus. Our native cattails represent the reeds used as rods in Bible stories. For the rushes of Isaiah's prophecy (Isa. 35:7), use the flowering rush *(Butomus umbellatus),* with its clusters of rose flowers.

FLAG

Sink a 21 x 21, 24 x 11, or 24 x 45 x 12 cedar or metal tub six inches below the ground level of your terrace. Edge it with stones or bricks for Baltic ivy to climb on. Place four inches of rich garden soil in the tub. Dealers can give supplies and directions for planting before you fill the tub with water.

In a small tub, plant only two hardy water lilies or one pink lotus of the Nile. To all tubs, add snails (as scavengers), oxygenating plants, and a special fertilizer at intervals. During winter, cover the tub with boards banked with straw. In the spring, dip out the water, remove all rubbish, and add fresh water.

MYRTLE AND OLEANDER
AS TERRACE PLANTS

Your porch or terrace can be greatly enhanced by tubs or boxes of Bible shrubs with flowers or fragrant leaves. The true myrtle *(Myrtus communis)* is a three- to five-foot evergreen shrub of exceedingly sweet odor, which was the emblem of divine generosity in religious ceremonies of the Jews before and after the Babylonian exile. When the Feast of the Tabernacle was established in 445 B.C., branches of myrtle and other evergreens were prescribed for arbors erected on the flat housetops (see Neh. 8:14-16). Myrtle wood was hard and useful in carved ornaments. Oil from the leaves and from its pink and white flowers is used today in perfume. In classical Greece and Judea, heroes were crowned with wreaths of its dark green leaves.

MYRTLE

Plant myrtle in a soil mixture of ⅓ topsoil, ⅓ leaf mold or humus, and ⅓ sharp sand over pebbles, adding a teaspoon of plant food and ½ teaspoon bone meal to a six-inch potful. It thrives if well watered when set outdoors in summer and mulched with plant food. It can be trimmed to a formal shape if desired. Keep it in a light, cool place indoors in winter, as it is not hardy in cold climates.

OLEANDER

The common oleander *(Nerium oleander)* takes the same soil and care. It is a native waterside shrub of prehistoric Palestine, growing there in such density along streams today

37

CYCLAMEN

that travelers, seeing its prolific bloom of pink flowers from June to October, exclaim over the spectacle. No wonder Ecclesiasticus 39:13 bids the Hebrews to "bud like a rose that grows by a watercourse." Modern varieties come not only with pink or white flowers, but also with salmon or yellow or crimson.

A RAISED BORDER OF BIBLE PLANTS

ROSE

Somewhere within view of your windows or terrace, build a raised bed six inches high, edged with brick or stones and filled with good topsoil. In the fall, plant at the front a low ground cover of Our Lady's bed straw (Galium verum), such as the hay on which Mary slept in the stable. It has yellow flowers and fragrant leaves. Intersperse this with Viola odorata, which smells like violets, and with the rosy-red flowers of miniature tubrous Cyclamen Europeam. The cyclamen needs winter protection.

At the rear of each end of the bed, plant the rose of Damascus with lupines and peonies. All the above are known to have grown wild in Judea. Near the center, plant garden heliotrope (Valeriana officinalis)—around a few bulbs of scarlet Turks cap or purple martagon lily, which grew in Solomon's garden.

In the spring, annuals may be sown behind the edging plants.

LUPINE

BIBLE TREES AND SHRUBS FOR THE YARD

CEDAR

ALMOND

If you have space for the noble, slow-growing evergreen cedar of Lebanon, a hardy variety is available. Another large tree that grew in Solomon's garden is the walnut, listed as the English walnut. It needs rich, moist soil.

For a smaller tree that thrives anywhere, try a poplar with quaking leaves, such as the Lombardy poplar or the quaking aspen (Populus tremuloides), which David had in mind (experts agree) in I Chronicles 14:14-15. Our hardy American redbud (Cersis canadensis) is related to the Asiatic redbud of Bible times, which legend says blushed in shame at Judas' betrayal—thus its rosy blossoms in April. Our flowering almond (Prunus glandulosa) is a relative of the almond tree of semitropical climates, which produced the nuts Jacob sent as a gift to Egypt (Gen. 43:11). Its pink or white flowers symbolized, as spring arrived in Israel, the fulfillment of God's promise. It takes light, well-drained soil that slopes away from the bush. Also try the Russian olive tree.

Tamarisk trees grew in the dry, seaside areas of Palestine, as in Beersheba, where Abraham planted "a grove" the botanists think was of tamarisk (Gen. 21:33). It is a small graceful tree, hardy as far north as Boston, with feathery sprays of pink flowers in April or July. Another attractive hardy lawn shrub is the Japanese snowbell, called *storax* or *styrax*. Its fragrant white bellflowers bloom in June. The Bible variety exuded the perfumed gum *stacte,* mentioned in Exodus 30:34. Give it light, porous soil.

TAMARISK

STYRAX